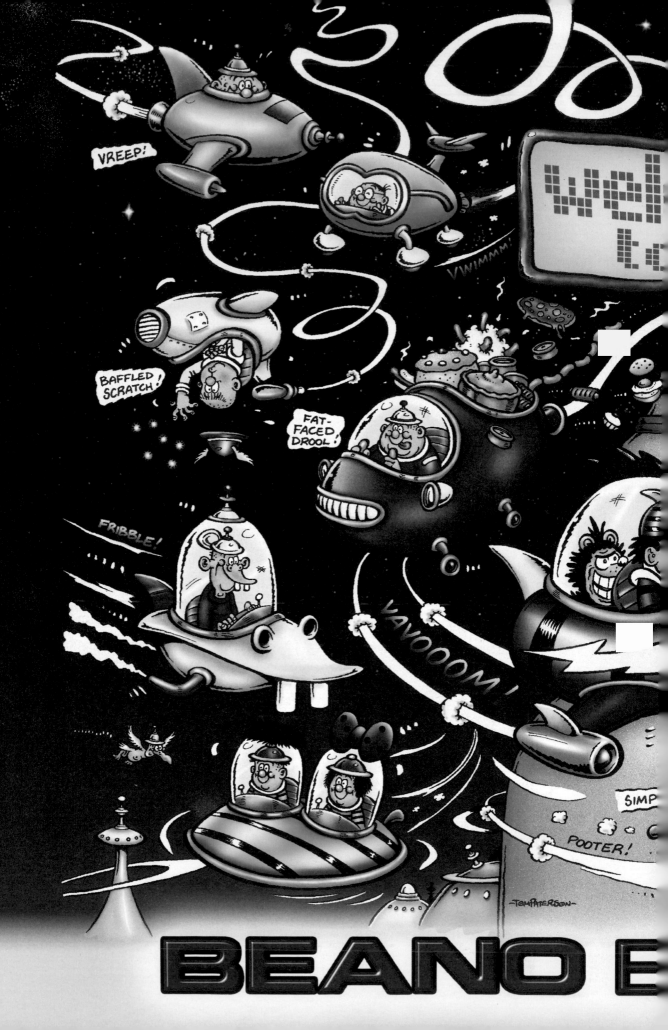

The Bash Street Kids

MUST FIND SOMETHING INTERESTING TO DO BEFORE WE GO TO SCHOOL.

GRAND OPENING

WOW! A GREAT NEW BALLOON FACTORY.

SHOW US ROUND, MISTER. PUH-LEEZE.

IN YOU POP!

POP! GOOD JOKE.

HERE, WE CAN MAKE ANY KIND OF BALLOON FOR ANYONE.

AND WE TEST THEM ALL!

THE BALLOON PASSED ITS BANGINESS TEST.

BANG!

MINNIE THE MINX

I HAVE SPRINGS – YOU CAN HAVE LOTS OF FUN WITH SPRINGS!

AH, THERE'S NOTHING LIKE A NICE READ OF THE PAPER IN A NICE, COMFY SEAT.

WRINKLIES WEEKLY? WORRIED? YOU'VE REASON TO BE.

AND THIS IS NOTHING LIKE A NICE READ OF THE PAPER IN A NICE, COMFY SEAT! WHO'S BEEN MESSING WITH MY CHAIR – AS IF I COULDN'T GUESS!

MINNIE!

DAD'S FOUND WHERE I GOT THE SPRINGS FROM HIS ARMCHAIR. AND THAT'S ONLY THE FIRST BIT OF FUN WITH SPRINGS!

SCUTTLE!

THIS IS A REALLY GREAT BIT OF FUN TO HAVE WITH SPRINGS – PAY ATTENTION NOW, READERS, I MAY ASK QUESTIONS LATER.

YOU GET A PIPE WITH A HOLE IN THE SIDE AND... PUFF... ONCE YOU PUSH THE SPRING DOWN PAST THE HOLE...

STRAIN!

WHAT IT LOOKS LIKE INSIDE

KEN. H. HARRISON.

DENNIS the MENACE

The NUMSKULLS

SIGH. EDD'S IN ONE OF HIS BORING MOODS. IT'S NO FUN FOR US.

BRAIN DEPT.

OO! THE PAINT ON THE FENCE IS DRYING. OO! THERE'S ANOTHER DRY BIT.

LEAVE THIS TO BRAINY. I'LL MAKE EDD GO A BIT WILD.

TAP! TAP!

THIS SUGGESTION SHOULD GET HIM GOING.

GO AND GET A TATTOO!

COOL IDEA, BRAINY.

EDGY!

BRAIN DEPT.

I'VE HAD A SUDDEN URGE TO GET A TATTOO.

TATTOO YOU

Barry Glennard

WHAT TO DO IF...

...You can't get to sleep!

GRUNT! HUMPH!

SHAKE SHAKE TURN

IT'S NO USE ...

... I CAN'T GET TO SLEEP!

I KNOW, I'LL COUNT SHEEP. ONE ... ER ... ONE ... THAT'S ALL I HAVE!

DEREK THE SHEEP DOLL

ZZZIP

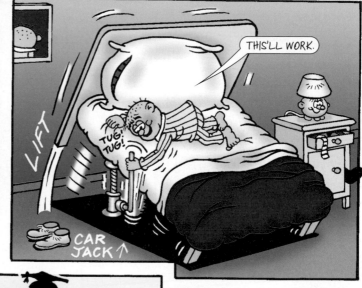

THIS'LL WORK.

LIFT

TUG! TUG!

CAR JACK ↑

OUCH! WELL, I DROPPED OFF BUT I DIDN'T GET TO SLEEP. THERE'S ONLY ONE THING FOR IT.

ROLL

T|H|U|M|P!

DRONE BLAH BLETHER BORE

BORING BOOK

Next morning, in class.

THE ONLY PLACE I ALWAYS GET TO SLEEP! ZZZZZZZ!

HEE- HEE!

DS

WHAT TO DO IF ...

... YOU NEED SELF PROTECTION!

LITTER
CUTHBERT CRINGEWORTHY

THE BASH STREET KIDS ARE ALWAYS PICKING ON ME – ESPECIALLY FATTY! BUT ALL THAT WILL CHANGE! HA! WHO SAYS BOOKS ARE FOR WIMPS?

BOOK WORLD

SELF-DEFENSE FOR BOOKWORMS AND SWOTS.

A KARATE CHOP? THERE DOESN'T SEEM TO BE ANYTHING HARD ABOUT THAT.

AAAAHHHHHH...

LEAP!

CHOP!

SLAAM!

...SORE! OKAY, THAT WAS PRETTY HARD – ON THE EARS!

OWOWOW!

THUD!

DEREK the SHEEP

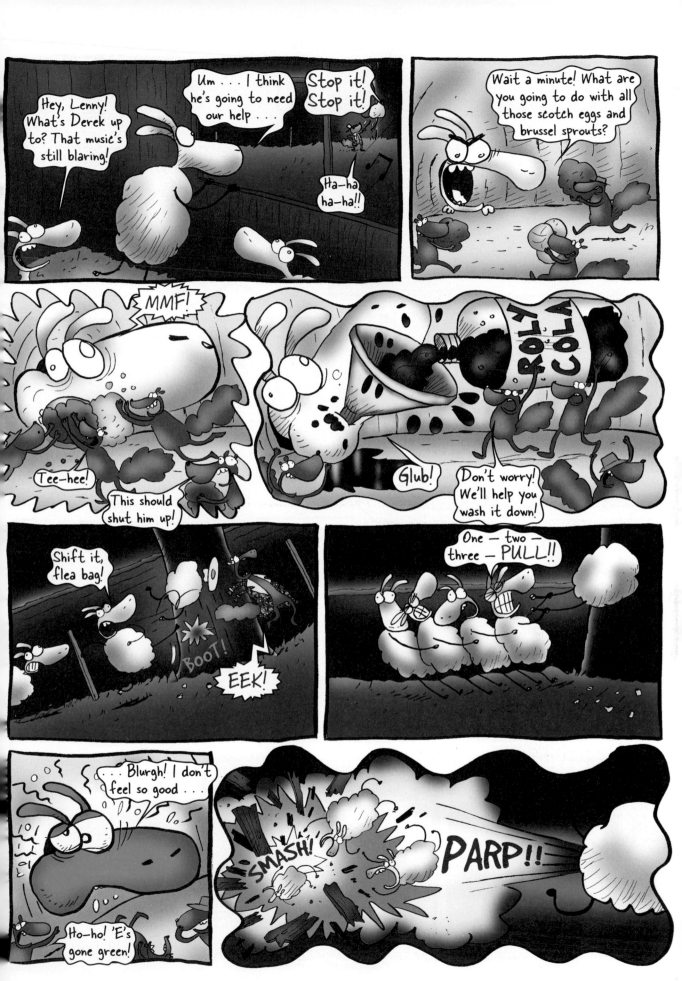

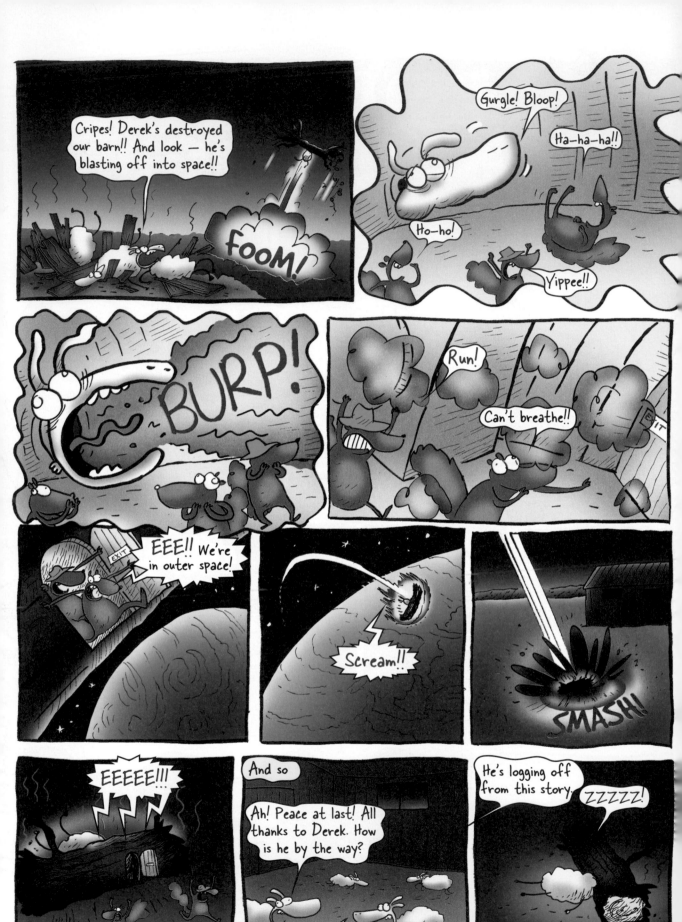

Beano Winter Olympic Games

RESULT LATER!

ROGER the DODGER

DODGE DREAMS!

DRONE! TONIGHT THERE WILL BE A...

...METEOR DISPLAY.

DID TEACHER SAY METEORS?

Suddenly paying attention.

TSK! THE CLASS TELESCOPE NEEDS A GOOD POLISH.

I'LL TAKE IT HOME AND POLISH IT, SIR!

HMM! ROGER'S TURNED OVER A NEW LEAF.

WHERE'S THE BRASS POLISH MUM?

GASP! ROGER USED THE WORD 'POLISH'!

Johnny Bean from HAPPY BUNNY GREEN

Farmer Farmer has a problem.

ARR. I DO.

Can you see what the problem is?

MY SCARECROW'S BLOOMING USELESS!

CAW!

Kind Johnny wants to help.

I'LL MAKE YOU A SCARECROW THAT'S GUARANTEED TO SCARE THE BIRDS.

GOOD LAD!

And earn some pocket money.

Johnny's setting to work.

So –

AHA! THERE THEY ARE!

GNEE – HEE!

GOTCHA!

EH?

WHUMMPH!

Not for long.

GNASH! GNASH!

MY DAD CAN BITE HIS WAY THROUGH ANYTHING!

HUMPH! YOU'LL NOT BE FREE FOR LONG. I'LL SEE TO THAT.

Later.

BEANO TOWN PARK

NO SIGN OF THAT PESKY DOG CATCHER.

GOOD! 'COS –

– I'VE JUST SPOTTED A BIG CAT!

GNIP! WATCH US CHASE IT!

POUNCE!

GRR!

GNASH! HE'S NOT MOVING?

Barry Glennard

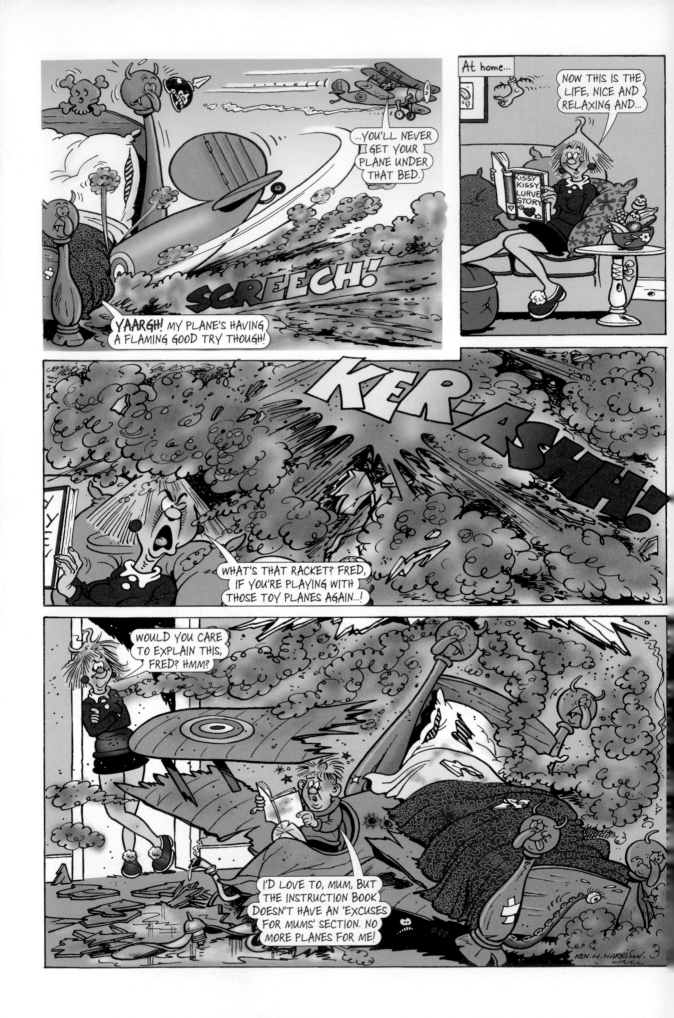

The Numskulls

WE NEED SOMEONE FOR THE 'INTERSCHOOL BRAINBOX CHALLENGE' TOMORROW!

TEECH

LOOK AT THIS PICTURE FOR TEN SECONDS, THEN I'LL ASK A QUESTION. WHOEVER GETS IT CORRECT WILL REPRESENT THE SCHOOL!

I'LL HELP EDD OUT.

EYE DEPT

CLICK!

WHIRR!

THE PICTURE'S GONE – HOW MANY PENGUINS WERE IN IT?

ONE, TWO, THREE...

QUICKLY NOW!

EYE DEPT

A TOTAL OF 357 PENGUINS!

I'LL TYPE IN THE ANSWER.

...357

357! I HAVE A PHOTOGRAPHIC MEMORY, SIR!

UNBELIEVABLE!

YOU'RE THE BOY FOR US!

GET STUDYING THE FACTS IN THAT BOOK AND WE'LL BE SURE TO WIN!

WELL CHUFFED!

HOOL

That night —

BETTER GIVE THESE A QUICK SCAN.

BUMPER BOOK OF FACTS

OH-OH! MY CAMERA'S BROKEN!

JAMMED!

THE FACTS ARE JUST NOT STAYING IN MY HEAD!

FRAZZLED SWEAT!

BU

TIME FOR ME TO STEP IN, BLINKY...

TOSS!

BIN

EYE DEPT.

...AND TRY OUT MY 'HOLOGRAPHIC FACT IMAGER'!

?

TRUNDLE! SQUEAK!

Many hours later –

I DON'T THINK MY HEAD CAN HOLD ANY MORE FACTS!

BUMPER BOOK OF FACTS

HE'S RIGHT! ALL THE MEMORY SPACE IN MY MACHINE IS USED UP.

FULL

BRAINBOX CHALLENGE

Next day –

OUR NEXT CONTESTANT IS REPRESENTING SLUDGE LANE SECONDARY.

QUIZMASTER

THIS IS OUR CHANCE FOR GLORY – WE'VE NEVER WON BEFORE!

NAME, PLEASE.

MY NAME IS...

...MARIE ANTOINETTE, WESTERN LOWLAND GORILLA, HAGGIS, THE MOON, EDAM CHEESE...

I THOUGHT HE WAS CLEVER BUT HE'S GOT A HEAD FULL OF NONSENSE!

HOOT! GUFFAW!

HAW-! HAW-!

–TOM PATERSON–

HAGGIS

WHAT A TIME FOR MY MACHINE TO BREAK DOWN!

FZZZT!

FZZZAAP!

WAAH!

In the present day, schoolchildren *William and Kathleen Grange* lead a secret life as costumed crime fighters...

BILLY the CAT and Katie

I FEAR WE ARE RATHER *LOST*, MY DEAR.

PERHAPS I SHOULD ASK ONE OF THESE *LOCALS* THE WAY TO THE *THEATRE*.

But in the fog shrouded streets of a bygone era, there was *another* crime fighter.

OHH! MY *BAG!*

THAT *RUFFIAN* HAS STOLEN MY *BAG!*

A hero who went by the name of...

I DON'T THINK THAT COLOUR *SUITS* YOU.

WILLIAM The Cat

as told by Mr. N. Dobbyn Esq.

UUUHH!

...NEWTON ROSEMERRY, THAT FIEND!

NOW, WILLIAM...

LORD ROSEMERRY IS A NOTED MEMBER OF THE ARISTOCRACY AND IS A GUEST IN OUR HOUSE. HE MUST BE TREATED WITH RESPECT.

BUT IF YOU ONLY KNEW WHAT I DO - THAT HE HAS HIS FINGER IN EVERY CRIMINAL ACTIVITY IN THIS TOWN - YOU WOULD THINK DIFFERENTLY.

MY APOLOGIES, LADY KATHLEEN. IT IS NOT RIGHT FOR A SERVANT TO OFFER AN OPINION.

OH, BILLY - DON'T BE LIKE THAT. YOU KNOW YOU'RE LIKE A BROTHER TO ME. AND CALL ME KATIE - YOU ONLY CALL ME LADY KATHLEEN WHEN YOU'RE ANGRY WITH ME.

I MUST ADMIT - I DO NOT THINK THAT FATHER LOOKS HAPPY AT LORD ROSEMERRY'S VISIT.

IF YOU HAD MY EXTRA SENSITIVE HEARING, YOU WOULD REALISE WHY.

I WILL NO LONGER STAND BY AND WATCH YOU UTILISE MY INVENTIONS FOR CRIMINAL GAIN. THAT WAS NEVER MY INTENTION WHEN YOU STARTED FUNDING MY RESEARCH!

WITHOUT MY MONEY, YOU WOULD NEVER HAVE AFFORDED TO CREATE ANYTHING. YOU WOULD NOT EVEN HAVE BEEN ABLE TO STAY IN THIS HOUSE.

YOU AND YOUR PRECIOUS DAUGHTER WOULD NOW BE LIVING ON THE STREETS!

LEAVE KATHLEEN OUT OF THIS. WE WILL FIND SOME WAY TO SURVIVE WITHOUT YOUR DIRTY MONEY.

I WANT YOU TO LEAVE MY HOUSE...

NOW!

IF YOU WILL NOT CONTINUE TO GIVE ME YOUR INVENTIONS VOLUNTARILY, I SHALL HAVE TO FIND SOME OTHER MEANS OF OBTAINING THEM.

MR. SPIKE, YOU HAVE YOUR ORDERS.

ARE YOU *ALRIGHT*, FATHER? WHAT IS...

SMAAASH!

NO! MY *AUTOMATON!* ROSEMERRY IS USING MY *OWN INVENTIONS* AGAINST ME!

WILLIAM, WE MUST *DO* SOMETHING!

WILLIAM...?

I ONLY HAVE *ONE CHANCE!* IF I CAN REACH THE *ROOF* IN TIME...

THE AUTOMATON IS MOVING *TOO FAST!* I'LL NEVER *MAKE IT!*

I HAVE TO *TRY!*

WILL WILLIAM MAKE IT? FIND OUT LATER IN THE BOOK.

MENACE-PUZZLE

treehouse

Find your way through Dennis's treehouse!

You've heard of the monkey-puzzle tree, but this is the menace-puzzle tree!

On each branch is a tricky puzzle for you to work out, but are you menace enough to solve them all?

Too-much Elm

E L M E E
M L E L L
E L M M M
L E L M L
M L E L E

This tree is suffering from Too-much Elm Disease. How many times can you find the word elm in this grid?

it all adds up!

1

A lot of birds live in the Menace-Puzzle tree. Can you find them all?

2

Complete these sequences of numbers

7, ___, 23, 31

3, 7, 11, ___

10, 8, ___, 4

Add ALL your answers together to find out how many times Dennis has been grounded this year!

TREE!

treesearch

Find all these species of tree in this wordsearch

rowan
oak
alder
ash
holly
beech
hawthorn
willow
pine
maple
cedar
chestnut

T	P	I	N	B	W	O	R	H
U	A	C	T	E	I	K	A	O
N	I	S	B	E	L	W	D	L
T	A	F	H	C	T	A	E	L
S	H	W	L	H	O	L	C	Y
E	P	A	O	N	H	D	H	O
H	I	R	Y	R	E	D	L	A
C	N	O	M	A	P	L	E	I
W	E	B	W	O	L	L	I	W

menacing Muddle!

Dennis uses the Menace-Puzzle tree to hide all his weapons of mass-menacing. Can you sort them all out from this muddle?

peashooterwaterbombcatapultwaterpistolstinkbombwhoopeecushion

DENNIS THE MENACE

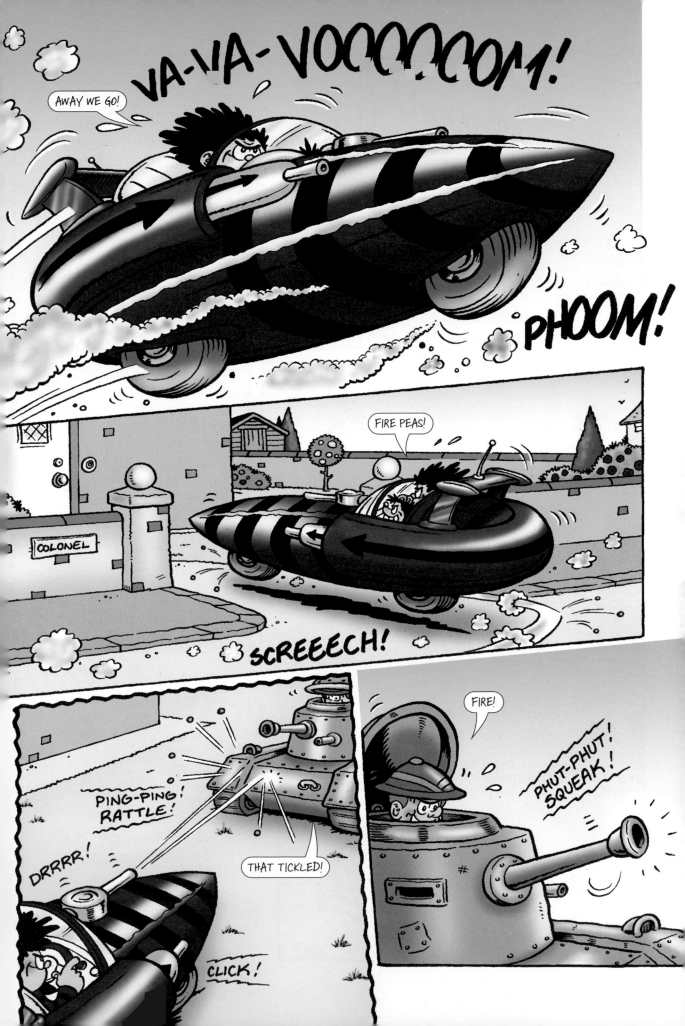

SPALOOSH!

WATER, ACTUALLY!

GLUB! TIME TO GET SNEAKY!

DRIP! SQUELCH!

TITTER! HOOT!

WE'LL TUNNEL OUR WAY IN!

SCRABBLE! SCRAPE! DIG!

TUNNELLING NOISES! BOY AND DOG COMING THIS WAY!

BIP! BIP!

DO WHAT YOU DO BEST, BEA!

PHWAAAARRP

CHUFF!

PHWOMP!

—TOM PATERSON—

And —

FLUMPH

SCRAPE

THERE ARE FUNNY NOISES COMING FROM THE HALL.

ELVIS FOUND!
"FALLEN DOWN BACK OF SOFA"

LES!

WHAT ON EARTH ARE YOU DOING?

I'M A MOLE AND I'M DIGGING A HOLE!

NOT IN MY NICE TIDY HOUSE, YOU'RE NOT!

OUTSIDE WHILE I CLEAN THIS UP.

WHAT A MESSY SON LES IS!

And –

IT TOOK ME AGES TO CLEAN THAT UP!

FRANKLY, MUM, THAT'S THE LEAST OF OUR WORRIES...

...CHECK OUT THE SIZE OF THAT MOLEHILL!

SHRIEK!

OUR HERO!

1. What page does this appear on?

2. How many residents of Happy Bunny Green are running away from Johnny Bean's giant scarecrow?

3. Whose spaceship is this?

5. Which Bash Street Kid balloon got stuck going through a door?

4. In the Ratz story about I Spy, which part of the body is Herman picking?

6. Who owns a Derek the Sheep cuddly toy?

7. Whose face is this?

8. Who is getting the "boot" in this picture?

9. How many people are in the water in the last pic of the Pirates story?

10. What is Minnie's cat, Chester, throwing into her Menace pipe?

12. Who is this?

11. Who is this a close-up of?

ARE YOU SMARTER THAN SMIFFY?

13. How many penguins did the Numskulls find in this picture?

14. What fell out of the sky and landed on Calamity James's head?

15. How many pairs of hotpants are on Biffo's washing line?

16. What should Cuthbert's books say?

BLITHER! TWITTER!

17. Who is carrying this box of chocs?

18. What is keeping Derek the sheep off his sleep?

19. How many people, including Roger, are in the Science Centre scene in Roger's Meteor story?

RIGHT, YOU LOT. SIT UP STRAIGHT AND OPEN THOSE LUGHOLES. I WANT TO SEE IF YOU'VE BEEN PAYING ATTENTION TO THIS BEANO BOOK, SO IT'S QUIZ TIME!

20. Who won this trophy?

2-MAN BOB WINNER 2008

Aiken Drum

AN OLD SCOTTISH NONSENSE SONG drawn by HUNT EMERSON

There was a man lived in the moon,
Lived in the moon, lived in the moon,
There was a man lived in the moon -

And his name was Aiken Drum!

And he played upon a ladle,
A ladle, a ladle,
He played upon a ladle,
And his name was
Aiken Drum!

SKWAWK
SKWONK

AIKEN DRUM - 1

And his hat was made of good cream cheese, Good cream cheese, Good cream cheese, His hat was made of good cream cheese -

And his name was **Aiken Drum!**

And his coat was made of good roast beef,

And his name was **Aiken Drum!**

And he played upon a ladle, A ladle, a ladle, He played upon a ladle - And his name was **Aiken Drum!**

And his buttons were made of penny loaves,

And his name was **Aiken Drum!**

And his breeks were made of haggis bags,

And his name was **Aiken Drum!**

AIKEN DRUM - 2

And he played upon a ladle,
A ladle, a ladle,
He played upon a ladle –
And his name was
Aiken Drum!

BONG
BONG
BONG
BONG

HOOTS HOOTS HOOTS HOOTS HOOTS HOOTS

BEANO

Aiken Drum is a traditional Scottish nonsense song. Like most folk songs, it's difficult to say where it came from, but it is thought that Aiken Drum dates from the Jacobite Rising of 1715. There are soldier's marching songs with the name "Aikendrum" in them, and a song about a soldier who gets covered in food, but he didn't play upon a ladle!

But who was Aiken Drum?

He may have been a Brownie – one of the Fairy People who lived in the mountains and glens.

Brownies were ugly, strange little monsters at first, but as time went by people became less superstitious, and Brownies became less frightening! By the time of the song they were more like clowns or comedy figures, and in modern times they are seen as Elves!

MOUNTAINS ARE THE BITS THAT GO UP!

GLENS ARE THE BITS THAT GO DOWN!

HANDSOME DEVIL!

After the beheading of King Charles I, and the English Civil Wars, the Jacobite Risings of 1715 and 1745 were part of the struggle by the supporters of the Scottish House of Stuart to get their kings back onto the Throne of England!

OUR KING'S BETTER THAN YOUR KING!

AWA' AND BILE YER HEED!

Scotland's best-known Brownie is in a poem called "The Brounie o' Blednoch" by William Nicholson (1825). He is called Aiken Drum – but he didn't play upon a ladle...

Aiken Drum is still sung by children today, but with more up-to-date words. You might know the version where his eyes are meatballs, his hair is a pizza, and his coat is custard!

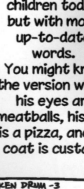

AIKEN DRUM -3

The BASH STREET KIDS

SIGH! WE'RE FED UP.

HUMPH! I'M FED UP!

Then —

SIR! SIR! THIS COULD BE THE ANSWER. A FREE HOLIDAY FOR A TEACHER AND PUPILS.

FREE HOLIDAY?

DAILY BLAH

YOU'RE RIGHT. AND WE CAN APPLY RIGHT HERE IN BEANOTOWN!

APPLY HERE FOR FREE HOLIDAY

WHAT IS THIS PLACE?

WE NEED A TEACHER AND PUPILS TO FLY INTO SPACE AND TRY OUT THE SPACE SCHOOL.

WE'LL DO IT.

YEAH!

YOU'LL NEED THOSE HEAVY BOOTS TO KEEP YOU ON THE FLOOR IN SPACE WHERE IT'S WEIGHTLESS.

HEAVY BOOTS - OKAY.

CLONK CLUNK

COO! IT'S DARK!

WHO'S GOT THE MAP?

HEH - HEH! THE AUTO - PILOT KNOWS THE WAY!

SICK BAG

LOOK! A SIGN POST!

SPACE SCHOOL 2,000,5000 MILES THIS WAY

FOLLOW ME, KIDS.

In the space classroom.

GREAT!

EXCELLENT! LET'S GET TO WORK AND TRY THIS PLACE OUT.

TUM ... TEE ... TUM.

TAP TAP

But –

YEAH!

SPLOOSH

FLOP BACK

THUD

GROO!

SPLASH

HO - HO! EVERYTHING IS WEIGHTLESS!

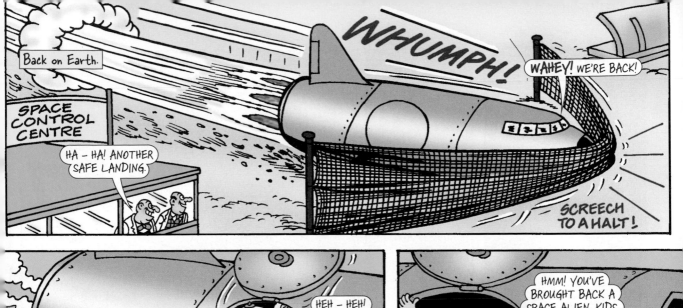

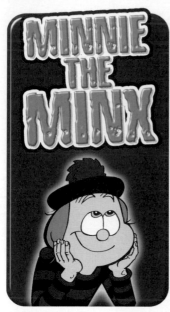

NIL
BY
MOUTH

MY POOR OLD DAD.

TONSIL WARD ←

I'M GONNA GIVE HIM A GREAT BIG HUGGY-HUG!

ZOOM!

SPIN!

IN GOES MIN!

AND OUT AGAIN!

SPIN!

CLATTER!

CRUNCH!

AWK!

POORLY COUGHS →

A MINX DOESN'T USE THE DOOR ANYWAY.

HEADACHES ←

OP THEATRE

OOH, THIS IS INTERESTING...

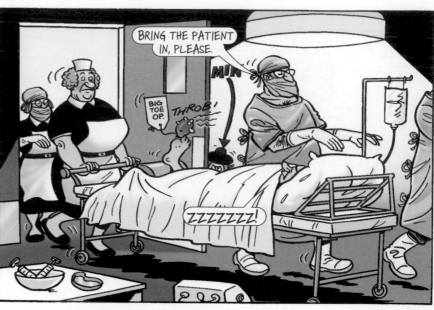

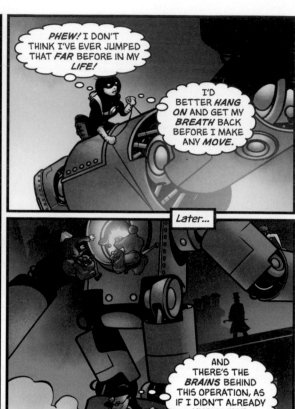

WHAT THE...? WHAT'S 'APPENED T'THE POWER?!

I'LL HAVE TO TIME THIS *JUST RIGHT.*

CRASH!

GET *OUT* OF HERE, LADY KATHLEEN. *I'LL* DEAL WITH THIS *VILLAIN.*

BUT I CAN...

PLEASE, LADY KATHLEEN, JUST *GO.* THIS IS NO PLACE FOR A *GIRL!*

IT LOOKS LIKE YOUR *CRONIES* ARE *OUT OF ACTION,* ROSEMERRY. I GUESS IT'S JUST DOWN TO *YOU AND ME.*

HMPH!

NOT *EXACTLY,* CAT BOY...

I NEVER TRAVEL *ANYWHERE* WITHOUT A LITTLE *BACKUP!*

CHIMNEY SWEEPS?!? YOU REALLY THINK YOU'RE GOING TO *STOP* ME WITH *CHIMNEY SWEEPS?*

HAAA!!!!!

oh....

YAH!

WHACK!

URRHH!

I THINK IT'S TIME *I* MADE A *STRATEGIC WITHDRAWAL.*

NOT SO *FAST,* 'LORD' ROSEMERRY.

AAAGH!

A *FRIEND* OF MINE TOLD ME YOU WEREN'T TO BE *TRUSTED.*

I SHOULD HAVE TRUSTED *HIM!*

NEED A HAND?

WHO...?

MADAM, *REALLY,* IT IS NOT *SEEMLY* FOR A *LADY* TO...

WHACK!

OOWWW!

YOU WERE SAYING?

ARE YOU BEANO MAD?

Are you upset now that you've nearly come to the end of this wicked annual? Well, never fear cos The Beano comes out every single week, so you'll never be bored again! Get on down to the shops every **Thursday** to see what **Dennis**, **Roger**, **Minnie** and the **gang** have been up to!

The biggest Beano fans EVER have joined the Beano Club! With lots of cool goodies when you join and your very own membership card – The Beano Club rocks! You can call: **0800 413 877** to join or log on to: www.beanotown.com!

Computer whizzes listen up! The Beanotown website is THE place to be. With lots of wicked games, a message board answered by one of the Beano crew, tons of secrets about your fave characters and much more you'll be on it for hours. Get on that web and check it out at

www.beanotown.com!

NO SOFTIES ALLOWED!

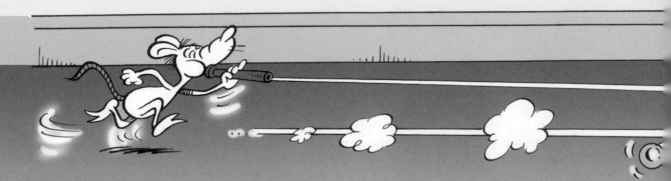